In the picture

Kevin was looking at one of his car books...

This car book is really good. It's got great pictures in it.

Look at this one.
It looks as if it was taken in Africa.
The car is miles from anywhere.
There are lions all around it, but
it's so clean it's gleaming!

Anyway, you could take pictures of cars.
I've got a camera somewhere.
You can use that.

I want to take pictures of cars.
Lots of people bring their cars to
Dad's garage for a service or for Dad to mend.
I'll see if there are any good cars at the garage.

I hope there are some good cars in today.

Kevin stayed at the garage for an hour, but no more good cars came along.

I'm fed up!
I want to take exciting pictures, but there's nothing happening.

You won't get much excitement here.
A garage is OK if you want to take
a picture of a tyre or an engine or a gear box.

11

15